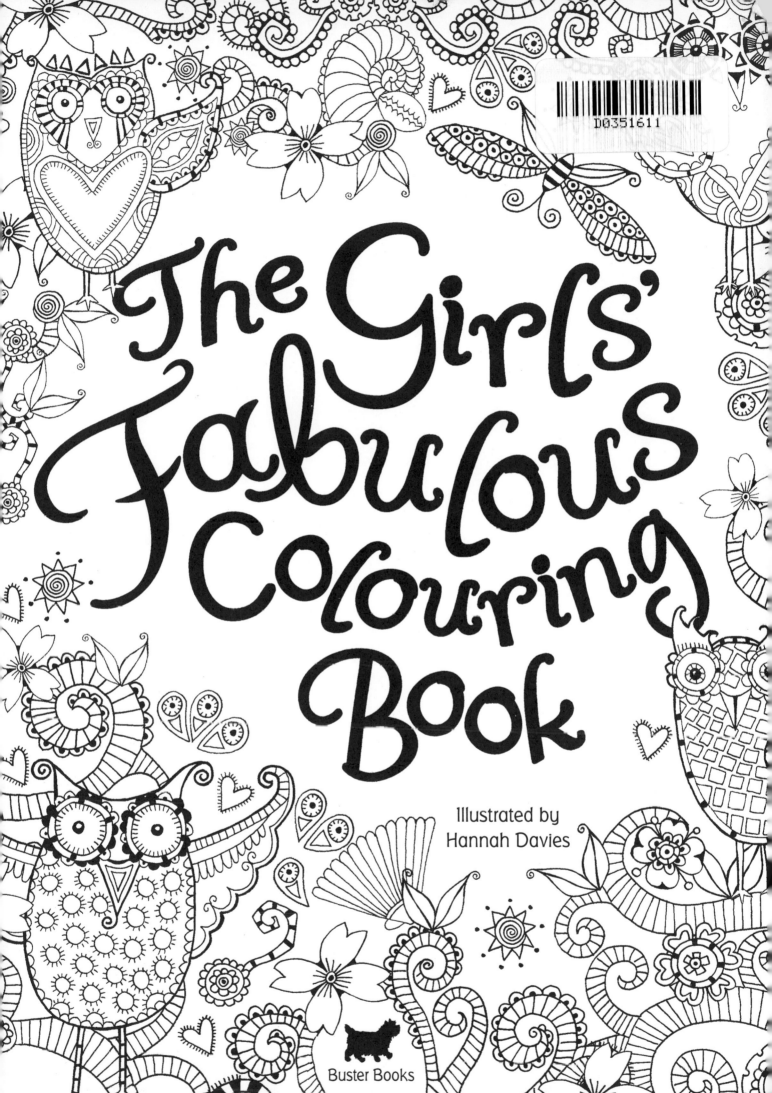

The Girls' Fabulous Colouring Book

Illustrated by
Hannah Davies

Buster Books

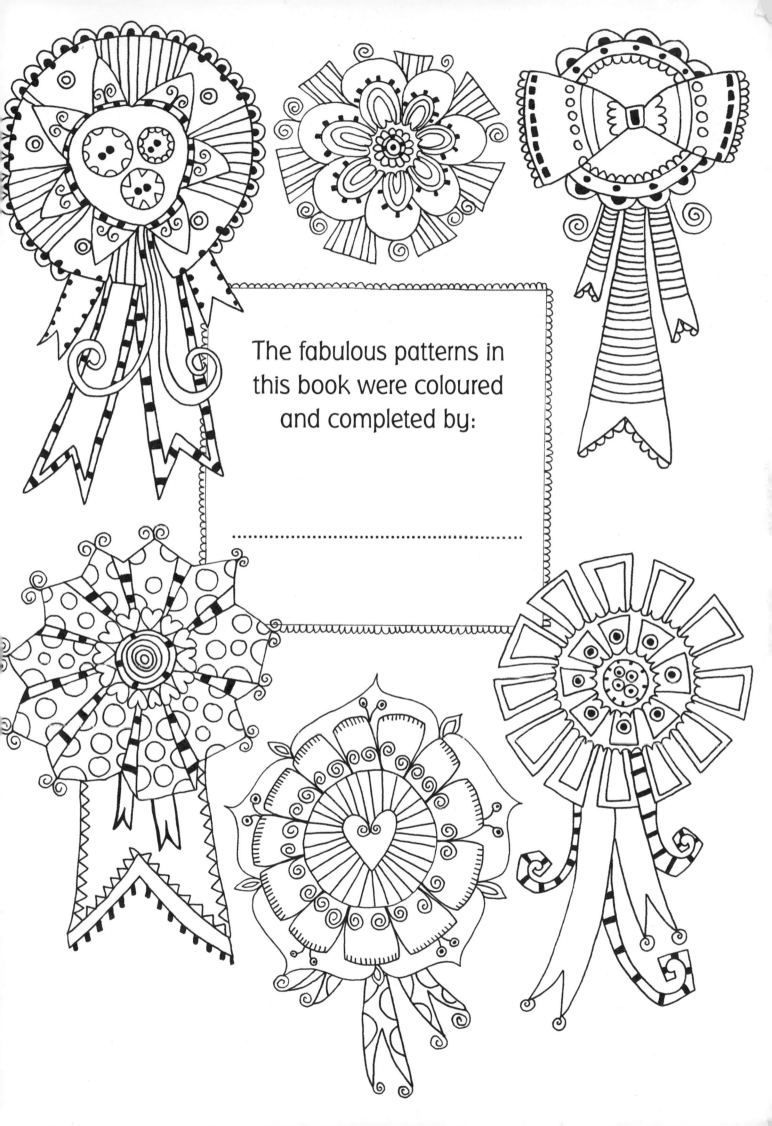

The fabulous patterns in
this book were coloured
and completed by:

....

Sherbet
Lemon Sweets
200g

Bon Bons

Rhubarb & Custard

Liquorice Allsorts 300g

Jell

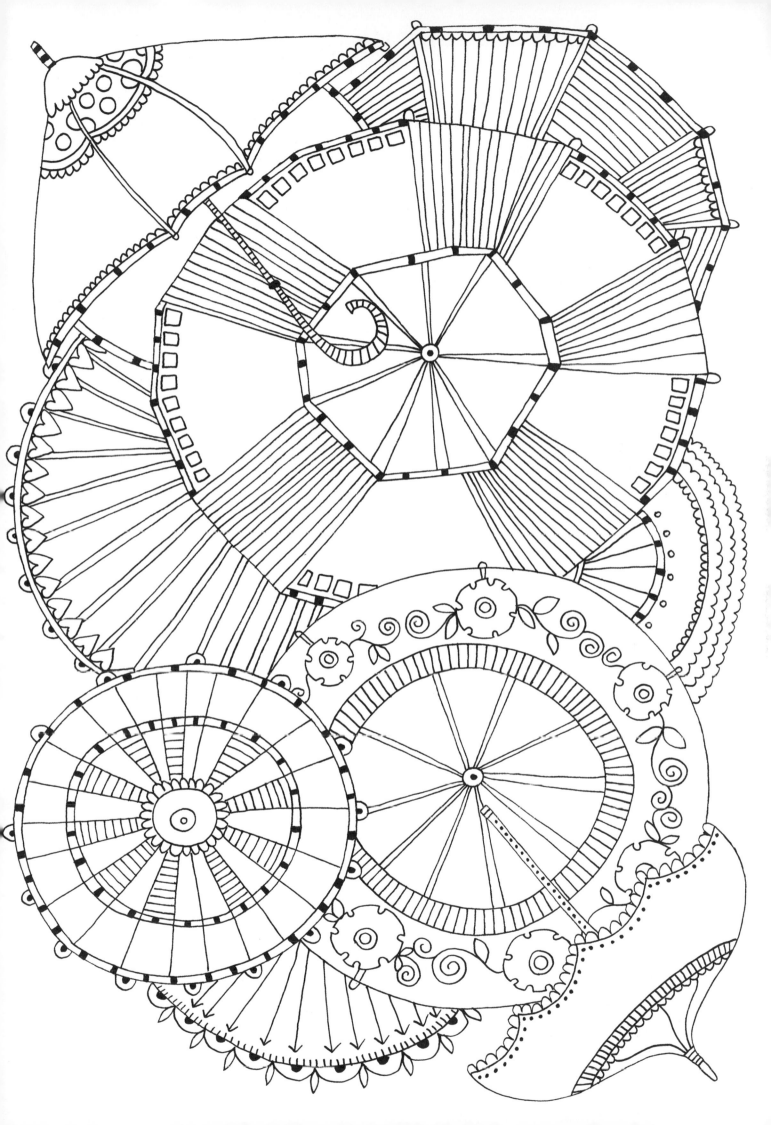

First published in Great Britain in 2012 by Buster Books,
an imprint of Michael O'Mara Books Limited,
9 Lion Yard, Tremadoc Road, London SW4 7NQ

W www.mombooks.com/buster f Buster Books y @BusterBooks

Copyright © 2012 Buster Books

ISBN: 978-1-78055-039-8

14 16 18 20 19 17 15 13

This book was printed in May 2020 by Leo Paper Products Ltd, Heshan Astros Printing Limited,
Xuantan Temple Industrial Zone, Gulao Town, Heshan City, Guangdong Province, China.